A Woman's

Catalog No. V270
Published by Pomegranate Communications, Inc.
Box 808022, Petaluma CA 94975

Available in Canada from Canadian Manda Group
165 Dufferin Street, Toronto, Ontario M6K 3H6

Available in the UK and mainland Europe from Pomegranate Europe Ltd.
Unit 1, Heathcote Business Centre, Hurlbutt Road, Warwick, Warwickshire CV34 6TD, UK

Available in Australia from Hardie Grant Books, 12 Claremont Street, South Yarra, Victoria 3141

Available in New Zealand from Southern Publishers Group, P.O. Box 8360, Symonds Street, Auckland

Available in the Far East from Julian Ashton, Ashton International Marketing Services
P.O. Box 298, Sevenoaks, Kent TN13 1WU, UK

Africa, Latin America, and the Middle East: info@pomegranate.com; 707-782-9000

Pomegranate also publishes the 2007 Susan Seddon Boulet calendars *Unicorns, Goddesses,* and *Shaman;* Cheryl Thiele's *Sacred Journey: Daily Journal for Your Soul;* and many other calendars in several formats. Our products and publications include books, posters, postcards and books of postcards, notecards and boxed notecard sets, magnets, mousepads, Knowledge Cards®, birthday books, journals, address books, jigsaw puzzles, designer gift wrap, stationery sets, and bookmarks. For more information or to place an order, please contact Pomegranate Communications, Inc.:
800-227-1428; www.pomegranate.com.

Cover image: *Eve,* n.d.

Designed by Ronni Madrid

Dates in color indicate federal holidays.
All astronomical data supplied in this calendar are expressed in Greenwich Mean Time (GMT).
Moon phases and American, Canadian, and UK holidays are noted.

● NEW MOON   ☽ FIRST QUARTER   ○ FULL MOON   ☾ LAST QUARTER

PAINTINGS BY Susan Seddon Boulet

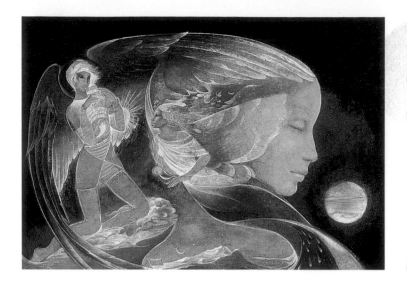

The past cannot be changed. The future is yet in your power.

Mary Pickford
The Women's Book of Positive Quotations, 2002

Untitled, 1979

LAST WEEK . . .
I enjoyed these blessings/triumphs

I faced these challenges/disappointments

THIS WEEK . . .
I will

I will hope for/pray for/meditate on

January

NEW YEAR'S DAY   *monday*

1 1

Today I feel . . .

BANK HOLIDAY (SCOTLAND)   *tuesday*

2 2

Today I feel . . .

wednesday

○ **3** 3

Today I feel . . .

thursday

4 4

Today I feel . . .

friday

5 5

Today I feel . . .

saturday

6 6

s	m	t	w	t	f	s
	1	2	3	4	5	6
7	8	9	10	11	12	13
14	15	16	17	18	19	20
21	22	23	24	25	26	27
28	29	30	31			

JANUARY

Today I feel . . .

sunday

7 7

Untitled, 1974

LAST WEEK . . .

I enjoyed these blessings/triumphs

I faced these challenges/disappointments

THIS WEEK . . .

I will

I will hope for/pray for/meditate on

January

Today I feel . . .

tuesday

9 9

Today I feel . . .

wednesday

10 10

Today I feel . . .

thursday

☾ **11** 11

Today I feel . . .

friday

12 12

Today I feel . . .

saturday

13 13

Today I feel . . .

sunday

14 14

s	m	t	w	t	f	s
	1	2	3	4	5	6
7	8	9	10	11	12	13
14	15	16	17	18	19	20
21	22	23	24	25	26	27
28	29	30	31			

JANUARY

Companions, 1992

LAST WEEK . . .
I enjoyed these blessings/triumphs

I faced these challenges/disappointments

THIS WEEK . . .
I will

I will hope for/pray for/meditate on

January

MARTIN LUTHER KING JR. DAY

monday

15 15

Today l feel . . .

tuesday

16 16

Today l feel . . .

wednesday

17 17

Today l feel . . .

thursday

18 18

Today l feel . . .

friday

● **19** 19

Today l feel . . .

saturday

20 20

Today l feel . . .

sunday

21 21

s	m	t	w	t	f	s
	1	2	3	4	5	6
7	8	9	10	11	12	13
14	15	16	17	18	19	20
21	22	23	24	25	26	27
28	29	30	31			

JANUARY

Untitled, 1976

D o not rely completely on any other human being . . . we meet all of life's greatest tests alone.

Agnes Macphail

The Women's Book of Positive Quotations, 2002

LAST WEEK . . .

I enjoyed these blessings/triumphs

I faced these challenges/disappointments

THIS WEEK . . .

I will

I will hope for/pray for/meditate on

January

monday

22 ₂₂

Today I feel . . .

tuesday

23 ₂₃

Today I feel . . .

wednesday

24 ₂₄

Today I feel . . .

thursday

☽ ## 25 ₂₅

Today I feel . . .

friday

26 ₂₆

Today I feel . . .

saturday

27 ₂₇

Today I feel . . .

sunday

28 ₂₈

s	m	t	w	t	f	s
	1	2	3	4	5	6
7	8	9	10	11	12	13
14	15	16	17	18	19	20
21	22	23	24	25	26	27
28	29	30	31			

JANUARY

N ever be afraid to sit
awhile and think.

Lorraine Hansberry
*The Women's Book of Positive
Quotations*, 2002

Untitled, 1974

LAST WEEK . . .

I enjoyed these blessings/triumphs

I faced these challenges/disappointments

THIS WEEK . . .

I will

I will hope for/pray for/meditate on

Jan ❧ Feb

Today I feel . . .

tuesday
30 ₃₀

Today I feel . . .

wednesday
31 ₃₁

Today I feel . . .

thursday
1 ₃₂

Today I feel . . .

friday
○ 2 ₃₃

Today I feel . . .

saturday
3 ₃₄

s	m	t	w	t	f	s
				1	2	3
4	5	6	7	8	9	10
11	12	13	14	15	16	17
18	19	20	21	22	23	24
25	26	27	28			

FEBRUARY

Today I feel . . .

sunday
4 ₃₅

When we are chafed and fretted by small cares, a look at the stars will show us the littleness of our own interests.

Maria Mitchell
The New Beacon Book of Quotations by Women, 1996

Untitled, 1974

LAST WEEK . . .
I enjoyed these blessings/triumphs

I faced these challenges/disappointments

THIS WEEK . . .
I will

I will hope for/pray for/meditate on

February

monday

5 ₃₆

Today I feel . . .

tuesday

6 ₃₇

Today I feel . . .

wednesday

7 ₃₈

Today I feel . . .

thursday

8 ₃₉

Today I feel . . .

friday

9 ₄₀

Today I feel . . .

saturday

☾ 10 ₄₁

Today I feel . . .

sunday

11 ₄₂

s	m	t	w	t	f	s
				1	2	3
4	5	6	7	8	9	10
11	12	13	14	15	16	17
18	19	20	21	22	23	24
25	26	27	28			

FEBRUARY

A person who has no secrets is a liar. We always fold ourselves away from others just enough to preserve a secret or two, something that we cannot share without destroying our inner landscape.

Ann Roiphe
The New Beacon Book of Quotations by Women, 1996

Untitled, 1976

LAST WEEK . . .
I enjoyed these blessings/triumphs

I faced these challenges/disappointments

THIS WEEK . . .
I will

I will hope for/pray for/meditate on

peaceful

February

LINCOLN'S BIRTHDAY

monday

12 43

Today I feel . . .

tuesday

13 44

Today I feel . . .

VALENTINE'S DAY

wednesday

14 45

Today I feel . . .

thursday

15 46

Today I feel . . .

friday

16 47

Today I feel . . .

saturday

● **17** 48

Today I feel . . .

sunday

18 49

s	m	t	w	t	f	s
				1	2	3
4	5	6	7	8	9	10
11	12	13	14	15	16	17
18	19	20	21	22	23	24
25	26	27	28			

FEBRUARY

Flight is nothing but an attitude in motion.

Diane Ackerman

The New Beacon Book of Quotations by Women, 1996

Pegasus, 1982

LAST WEEK . . .

I enjoyed these blessings/triumphs

I faced these challenges/disappointments

THIS WEEK . . .

I will

I will hope for/pray for/meditate on

February

PRESIDENTS' DAY

monday

19 50

Today I feel . . .

tuesday

20 51

Today I feel . . .

ASH WEDNESDAY

wednesday

21 52

Today I feel . . .

WASHINGTON'S BIRTHDAY

thursday

22 53

Today I feel . . .

friday

23 54

Today I feel . . .

saturday

☽ **24** 55

s	m	t	w	t	f	s
				1	2	3
4	5	6	7	8	9	10
11	12	13	14	15	16	17
18	19	20	21	22	23	24
25	26	27	28			

FEBRUARY

Today I feel . . .

sunday

25 56

H ere I am, where I ought
  to be.

Louise Erdrich
The Women's Book of Positive
Quotations, 2002

Illustration from *Buffalo Gals*,
by Ursula LeGuin, 1994

LAST WEEK . . .
I enjoyed these blessings/triumphs

I faced these challenges/disappointments

THIS WEEK . . .
I will

I will hope for/pray for/meditate on

monday

26 57

Today I feel . . .

tuesday

27 58

Today I feel . . .

wednesday

28 59

Today I feel . . .

thursday

1 60

Today I feel . . .

friday

2 61

Today I feel . . .

PURIM (BEGINS AT SUNSET)

saturday

○ **3** 62

Today I feel . . .

sunday

4 63

s	m	t	w	t	f	s
				1	2	3
4	5	6	7	8	9	10
11	12	13	14	15	16	17
18	19	20	21	22	23	24
25	26	27	28	29	30	31

MARCH

Ritual is the way we carry
the presence of the sacred.
Ritual is the spark that must not
go out.

Christina Baldwin
*The New Beacon Book of Quotations
by Women, 1996*

Ritual Mask, 1988

LAST WEEK . . .
I enjoyed these blessings/triumphs

I faced these challenges/disappointments

THIS WEEK . . .
I will

I will hope for/pray for/meditate on

march

monday

5 64

Today I feel . . .

tuesday

6 65

Today I feel . . .

wednesday

7 66

Today I feel . . .

INTERNATIONAL WOMEN'S DAY

thursday

8 67

Today I feel . . .

friday

9 68

Today I feel . . .

saturday

10 69

Today I feel . . .

DAYLIGHT SAVING TIME BEGINS

sunday

11 70

s	m	t	w	t	f	s
				1	2	3
4	5	6	7	8	9	10
11	12	13	14	15	16	17
18	19	20	21	22	23	24
25	26	27	28	29	30	31

MARCH

Each day, and the living of it, has to be a conscious creation in which discipline and order are relieved with some play and pure foolishness.

May Sarton
The Women's Book of Positive Quotations,
2002

Untitled, 1976

LAST WEEK . . .
I enjoyed these blessings/triumphs

I faced these challenges/disappointments

THIS WEEK . . .
I will

I will hope for/pray for/meditate on

March

monday

☾ **12** 71

Today I feel . . .

tuesday

13 72

Today I feel . . .

wednesday

14 73

Today I feel . . .

thursday

15 74

Today I feel . . .

friday

16 75

Today I feel . . .

ST. PATRICK'S DAY

saturday

17 76

Today I feel . . .

MOTHERING SUNDAY (UK)

sunday

18 77

s	m	t	w	t	f	s
				1	2	3
4	5	6	7	8	9	10
11	12	13	14	15	16	17
18	19	20	21	22	23	24
25	26	27	28	29	30	31

MARCH

It's better to be a lion for a day than a sheep all your life.

Elizabeth Kenny
The Women's Book of Positive Quotations, 2002

Untitled, 1978

LAST WEEK . . .
I enjoyed these blessings/triumphs

I faced these challenges/disappointments

THIS WEEK . . .
I will

I will hope for/pray for/meditate on

March

Today I feel . . .

Today I feel . . .

VERNAL EQUINOX 12:07 AM (GMT)

Today I feel . . .

Today I feel . . .

Today I feel . . .

s	m	t	w	t	f	s
				1	2	3
4	5	6	7	8	9	10
11	12	13	14	15	16	17
18	19	20	21	22	23	24
25	26	27	28	29	30	31

MARCH

Today I feel . . .

SUMMER TIME BEGINS (UK)

Untitled (Nephthys), 1979

Nobody has ever measured, even the poets, how much a heart can hold.

Zelda Fitzgerald
The New Beacon Book of Quotations by Women, 1996

LAST WEEK . . .
I enjoyed these blessings/triumphs

I faced these challenges/disappointments

THIS WEEK . . .
I will

I will hope for/pray for/meditate on

Mar ❦ Apr

monday

26 85

Today I feel . . .

tuesday

27 86

Today I feel . . .

wednesday

28 87

Today I feel . . .

thursday

29 88

Today I feel . . .

friday

30 89

Today I feel . . .

saturday

31 90

Today I feel . . .

PALM SUNDAY

sunday

1 91

s	m	t	w	t	f	s
1	2	3	4	5	6	7
8	9	10	11	12	13	14
15	16	17	18	19	20	21
22	23	24	25	26	27	28
29	30					

APRIL

Birds, 1980

LAST WEEK . . .
I enjoyed these blessings/triumphs

I faced these challenges/disappointments

THIS WEEK . . .
I will

I will hope for/pray for/meditate on

April

PASSOVER (BEGINS AT SUNSET)

monday

○ **2** 92

Today I feel . . .

tuesday

3 93

Today I feel . . .

wednesday

4 94

Today I feel . . .

thursday

5 95

Today I feel . . .
GOOD FRIDAY

friday

6 96

Today I feel . . .

saturday

7 97

s	m	t	w	t	f	s
1	2	3	4	5	6	7
8	9	10	11	12	13	14
15	16	17	18	19	20	21
22	23	24	25	26	27	28
29	30					

APRIL

Today I feel . . .
EASTER SUNDAY

sunday

8 98

Please know I am quite aware of the hazards. I want to do it because I want to do it. Women must try to do things as men have tried. When they fail, their failure must be but a challenge to others.

Amelia Earhart
The New Beacon Book of Quotations by Women, 1996

Night Rider, 1974

LAST WEEK . . .
I enjoyed these blessings/triumphs

I faced these challenges/disappointments

THIS WEEK . . .
I will

I will hope for/pray for/meditate on

April

EASTER MONDAY (CANADA, UK)

monday

9 99

Today l feel . . .

tuesday

☾ **10** 100

Today l feel . . .

wednesday

11 101

Today l feel . . .

thursday

12 102

Today l feel . . .

friday

13 103

Today l feel . . .

saturday

14 104

Today l feel . . .

sunday

15 105

s	m	t	w	t	f	s
1	2	3	4	5	6	7
8	9	10	11	12	13	14
15	16	17	18	19	20	21
22	23	24	25	26	27	28
29	30					

APRIL

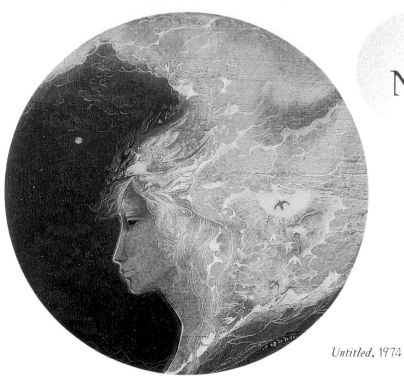

N ot all speed is movement.

Toni Cade
The Women's Book of Positive Quotations, 2002

Untitled, 1974

LAST WEEK . . .
I enjoyed these blessings/triumphs

I faced these challenges/disappointments

THIS WEEK . . .
I will

I will hope for/pray for/meditate on

deep

cozy

April

monday

16 106

Today I feel . . .

tuesday

● **17** 107

Today I feel . . .

wednesday

18 108

Today I feel . . .

thursday

19 109

Today I feel . . .

friday

20 110

Today I feel . . .

saturday

21 111

Today I feel . . .

EARTH DAY

sunday

22 112

s	m	t	w	t	f	s
1	2	3	4	5	6	7
8	9	10	11	12	13	14
15	16	17	18	19	20	21
22	23	24	25	26	27	28
29	30					

APRIL

There is no doubt that running away on a fresh, blue morning can be exhilarating.

Jean Rhys
The New Beacon Book of Quotations by Women, 1996

Untitled, 1978

LAST WEEK . . .
I enjoyed these blessings/triumphs

I faced these challenges/disappointments

THIS WEEK . . .
I will

I will hope for/pray for/meditate on

April

monday

23 113

Today I feel . . .

tuesday

☽ **24** 114

Today I feel . . .

wednesday

25 115

Today I feel . . .

thursday

26 116

Today I feel . . .

friday

27 117

Today I feel . . .

saturday

28 118

Today I feel . . .

sunday

29 119

s	m	t	w	t	f	s
1	2	3	4	5	6	7
8	9	10	11	12	13	14
15	16	17	18	19	20	21
22	23	24	25	26	27	28
29	30					

APRIL

Crone, 1987

LAST WEEK . . .
I enjoyed these blessings/triumphs

I faced these challenges/disappointments

THIS WEEK . . .
I will

I will hope for/pray for/meditate on

Apr ❧ May

monday

30 120

Today I feel . . .

tuesday

1 121

Today I feel . . .

wednesday

○ ## 2 122

Today I feel . . .

thursday

3 123

Today I feel . . .

friday

4 124

Today I feel . . .

CINCO DE MAYO

saturday

5 125

Today I feel . . .

sunday

6 126

s	m	t	w	t	f	s
		1	2	3	4	5
6	7	8	9	10	11	12
13	14	15	16	17	18	19
20	21	22	23	24	25	26
27	28	29	30	31		

MAY

The thing women have got to
learn is that nobody gives
you power. You just take it.

Roseanne Barr

The Women's Book of Positive Quotations,
2002

Fire Mask, 1976

LAST WEEK . . .

I enjoyed these blessings/triumphs

I faced these challenges/disappointments

THIS WEEK . . .

I will

I will hope for/pray for/meditate on

BANK HOLIDAY (UK)

monday

7 ₁₂₇

Today I feel . . .

tuesday

8 ₁₂₈

Today I feel . . .

wednesday

9 ₁₂₉

Today I feel . . .

thursday

☾ **10** ₁₃₀

Today I feel . . .

friday

11 ₁₃₁

Today I feel . . .

saturday

12 ₁₃₂

Today I feel . . .

MOTHER'S DAY

sunday

13 ₁₃₃

s	m	t	w	t	f	s
		1	2	3	4	5
6	7	8	9	10	11	12
13	14	15	16	17	18	19
20	21	22	23	24	25	26
27	28	29	30	31		

MAY

It is to please herself that the cat purrs.

Irish proverb
The Women's Book of Positive Quotations, 2002

Untitled, 1979

LAST WEEK . . .
I enjoyed these blessings/triumphs

I faced these challenges/disappointments

THIS WEEK . . .
I will

I will hope for/pray for/meditate on

May

monday

14 134

Today I feel . . .

tuesday

15 135

Today I feel . . .

wednesday

● **16** 136

Today I feel . . .

thursday

17 137

Today I feel . . .

friday

18 138

Today I feel . . .

ARMED FORCES DAY

saturday

19 139

Today I feel . . .

sunday

20 140

s	m	t	w	t	f	s
		1	2	3	4	5
6	7	8	9	10	11	12
13	14	15	16	17	18	19
20	21	22	23	24	25	26
27	28	29	30	31		

MAY

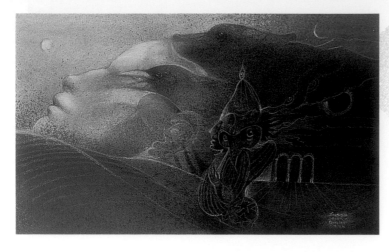

Cirque, 1994

It is in our idleness, in our dreams, that the submerged
truth sometimes comes to the top.

Virginia Woolf
The Women's Book of Positive Quotations, 2002

LAST WEEK . . .
I enjoyed these blessings/triumphs

I faced these challenges/disappointments

THIS WEEK . . .
I will

I will hope for/pray for/meditate on

May

VICTORIA DAY (CANADA)

monday

21 141

Today I feel . . .

tuesday

22 142

Today I feel . . .

wednesday

☽ **23** 143

Today I feel . . .

thursday

24 144

Today I feel . . .

friday

25 145

Today I feel . . .

saturday

26 146

Today I feel . . .

sunday

27 147

s	m	t	w	t	f	s
		1	2	3	4	5
6	7	8	9	10	11	12
13	14	15	16	17	18	19
20	21	22	23	24	25	26
27	28	29	30	31		

MAY

Untitled, 1978

LAST WEEK . . .
I enjoyed these blessings/triumphs

I faced these challenges/disappointments

THIS WEEK . . .
I will

I will hope for/pray for/meditate on

MEMORIAL DAY OBSERVED
BANK HOLIDAY (UK)

monday

28 148

Today I feel . . .

tuesday

29 149

Today I feel . . .

MEMORIAL DAY

wednesday

30 150

Today I feel . . .

thursday

31 151

Today I feel . . .

friday

◯ **1** 152

Today I feel . . .

saturday

2 153

Today I feel . . .

sunday

3 154

s	m	t	w	t	f	s
					1	2
3	4	5	6	7	8	9
10	11	12	13	14	15	16
17	18	19	20	21	22	23
24	25	26	27	28	29	30

JUNE

H iding leads nowhere except
to more hiding.

Margaret A. Robinson
*The New Beacon Book of Quotations
by Women, 1996*

Untitled, 1975

LAST WEEK . . .
I enjoyed these blessings/triumphs

I faced these challenges/disappointments

THIS WEEK . . .
I will

I will hope for/pray for/meditate on

June

monday

4   155

Today I feel . . .

tuesday

5   156

Today I feel . . .

wednesday

6   157

Today I feel . . .

thursday

7   158

Today I feel . . .

friday

☾ 8   159

Today I feel . . .

saturday

9   160

Today I feel . . .

sunday

10   161

s	m	t	w	t	f	s
					1	2
3	4	5	6	7	8	9
10	11	12	13	14	15	16
17	18	19	20	21	22	23
24	25	26	27	28	29	30

JUNE

Sorrow has its reward. It never leaves us where it found us.

Mary Baker Eddy
The New Beacon Book of Quotations by Women, 1996

Untitled, 1974

LAST WEEK . . .
I enjoyed these blessings/triumphs

I faced these challenges/disappointments

THIS WEEK . . .
I will

I will hope for/pray for/meditate on

June

monday

11 ₁₆₂

Today I feel . . .

tuesday

12 ₁₆₃

Today I feel . . .

wednesday

13 ₁₆₄

Today I feel . . .

FLAG DAY

thursday

14 ₁₆₅

Today I feel . . .

friday

 15 ₁₆₆

Today I feel . . .

saturday

16 ₁₆₇

Today I feel . . .

FATHER'S DAY

sunday

17 ₁₆₈

s	m	t	w	t	f	s
					1	2
3	4	5	6	7	8	9
10	11	12	13	14	15	16
17	18	19	20	21	22	23
24	25	26	27	28	29	30

JUNE

You never conquer a mountain.
You stand on the summit a
few moments; then the wind blows
your footprints away.

Arlene Blum
The Women's Book of Positive Quotations,
2002

Buffalo Woman, 1991

LAST WEEK . . .
l enjoyed these blessings/triumphs

l faced these challenges/disappointments

THIS WEEK . . .
l will

l will hope for/pray for/meditate on

June

Today I feel . . .

tuesday

19 170

Today I feel . . .

wednesday

20 171

Today I feel . . .

SUMMER SOLSTICE 6:06 PM (GMT)

thursday

21 172

Today I feel . . .

friday

☽ **22** 173

Today I feel . . .

saturday

23 174

Today I feel . . .

sunday

24 175

s	m	t	w	t	f	s
					1	2
3	4	5	6	7	8	9
10	11	12	13	14	15	16
17	18	19	20	21	22	23
24	25	26	27	28	29	30

JUNE

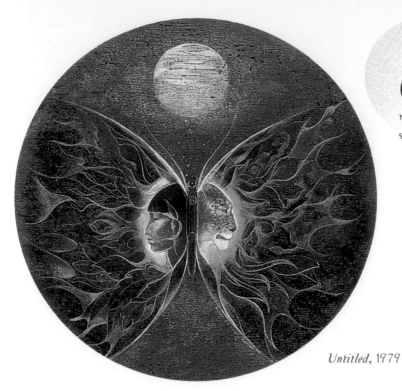

Contradiction itself, far from always being a criterion of error, is sometimes a sign of truth.

Simone Weil
The New Beacon Book of Quotations by Women, 1996

Untitled, 1979

LAST WEEK . . .

I enjoyed these blessings/triumphs

I faced these challenges/disappointments

THIS WEEK . . .

I will

I will hope for/pray for/meditate on

monday

25 176

Today I feel . . .

tuesday

26 177

Today I feel . . .

wednesday

27 178

Today I feel . . .

thursday

28 179

Today I feel . . .

friday

29 180

Today I feel . . .

saturday

○ **30** 181

Today I feel . . .

CANADA DAY (CANADA)

sunday

1 182

s	m	t	w	t	f	s
1	2	3	4	5	6	7
8	9	10	11	12	13	14
15	16	17	18	19	20	21
22	23	24	25	26	27	28
29	30	31				

JULY

Untitled, 1976

LAST WEEK . . .

I enjoyed these blessings/triumphs

I faced these challenges/disappointments

THIS WEEK . . .

I will

I will hope for/pray for/meditate on

July

CANADA DAY OBSERVED (CANADA)

monday

2 ₁₈₃

Today I feel . . .

tuesday

3 ₁₈₄

Today I feel . . .

INDEPENDENCE DAY

wednesday

4 ₁₈₅

Today I feel . . .

thursday

5 ₁₈₆

Today I feel . . .

friday

6 ₁₈₇

Today I feel . . .

saturday

☾ 7 ₁₈₈

Today I feel . . .

sunday

8 ₁₈₉

s	m	t	w	t	f	s
1	2	3	4	5	6	7
8	9	10	11	12	13	14
15	16	17	18	19	20	21
22	23	24	25	26	27	28
29	30	31				

JULY

Untitled, 1974

Adventure is worthwhile in itself.

Amelia Earhart
Great Quotes from Great Women, 1997

LAST WEEK . . .
I enjoyed these blessings/triumphs

I faced these challenges/disappointments

THIS WEEK . . .
I will

I will hope for/pray for/meditate on

July

monday

9 190

Today I feel . . .

tuesday

10 191

Today I feel . . .

wednesday

11 192

Today I feel . . .

BANK HOLIDAY (N. IRELAND)

thursday

12 193

Today I feel . . .

friday

13 194

Today I feel . . .

saturday

● **14** 195

s	m	t	w	t	f	s
1	2	3	4	5	6	7
8	9	10	11	12	13	14
15	16	17	18	19	20	21
22	23	24	25	26	27	28
29	30	31				

JULY

Today I feel . . .

sunday

15 196

No one can figure out your worth but you.

Pearl Bailey
The Women's Book of Positive Quotations,
2002

Empress III, 1975

LAST WEEK . . .
I enjoyed these blessings/triumphs

I faced these challenges/disappointments

THIS WEEK . . .
I will

I will hope for/pray for/meditate on

July

monday

16 197

Today I feel . . .

tuesday

17 198

Today I feel . . .

wednesday

18 199

Today I feel . . .

thursday

19 200

Today I feel . . .

friday

20 201

Today I feel . . .

saturday

21 202

Today I feel . . .

sunday

☽ **22** 203

s	m	t	w	t	f	s
1	2	3	4	5	6	7
8	9	10	11	12	13	14
15	16	17	18	19	20	21
22	23	24	25	26	27	28
29	30	31				

JULY

Mirrors, 1994

Nature gives you the face you have at twenty; it is
up to you to merit the face you have at fifty.

Coco Chanel

The New Beacon Book of Quotations by Women, 1996

LAST WEEK . . .
I enjoyed these blessings/triumphs

I faced these challenges/disappointments

THIS WEEK . . .
I will

I will hope for/pray for/meditate on

July

monday
23 204

Today I feel . . .

tuesday
24 205

Today I feel . . .

wednesday
25 206

Today I feel . . .

thursday
26 207

Today I feel . . .

friday
27 208

Today I feel . . .

saturday
28 209

Today I feel . . .

sunday
29 210

s	m	t	w	t	f	s
1	2	3	4	5	6	7
8	9	10	11	12	13	14
15	16	17	18	19	20	21
22	23	24	25	26	27	28
29	30	31				

JULY

No object is mysterious. The mystery is your eye.

Elizabeth Bowen

The New Beacon Book of Quotations by Women, 1996

Aphrodite, 1977

LAST WEEK . . .

I enjoyed these blessings/triumphs

I faced these challenges/disappointments

THIS WEEK . . .

I will

I will hope for/pray for/meditate on

Jul ❧ Aug

monday

◯ **30** ₂₁₁

Today I feel . . .

tuesday

31 ₂₁₂

Today I feel . . .

wednesday

1 ₂₁₃

Today I feel . . .

thursday

2 ₂₁₄

Today I feel . . .

friday

3 ₂₁₅

Today I feel . . .

saturday

4 ₂₁₆

Today I feel . . .

sunday

☾ **5** ₂₁₇

s	m	t	w	t	f	s
			1	2	3	4
5	6	7	8	9	10	11
12	13	14	15	16	17	18
19	20	21	22	23	24	25
26	27	28	29	30	31	

AUGUST

When you look up from your typewriter, look at the trees, not the calendar.

Mary Virginia Micka
*The New Beacon Book of Quotations
by Women*, 1996

Untitled, 1974

LAST WEEK . . .
I enjoyed these blessings/triumphs

I faced these challenges/disappointments

THIS WEEK . . .
I will

I will hope for/pray for/meditate on

August

CIVIC HOLIDAY (CANADA, MOST PROVINCES) *monday*
BANK HOLIDAY (SCOTLAND)

6 218

Today I feel . . .

tuesday

7 219

Today I feel . . .

wednesday

8 220

Today I feel . . .

thursday

9 221

Today I feel . . .

friday

10 222

Today I feel . . .

saturday

11 223

s	m	t	w	t	f	s
			1	2	3	4
5	6	7	8	9	10	11
12	13	14	15	16	17	18
19	20	21	22	23	24	25
26	27	28	29	30	31	

AUGUST

Today I feel . . .

sunday

● **12** 224

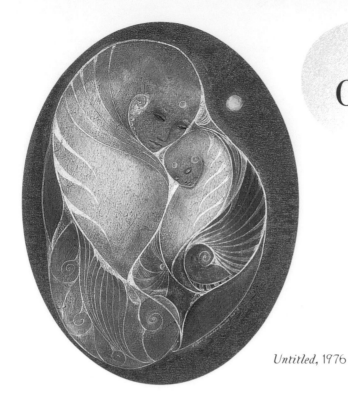

Conflict begins at the moment of birth.

Jean Baker Miller
The New Beacon Book of Quotations by Women, 1996

Untitled, 1976

LAST WEEK . . .
I enjoyed these blessings/triumphs

I faced these challenges/disappointments

THIS WEEK . . .
I will

I will hope for/pray for/meditate on

August

monday

13 225

Today I feel . . .

tuesday

14 226

Today I feel . . .

wednesday

15 227

Today I feel . . .

thursday

16 228

Today I feel . . .

friday

17 229

Today I feel . . .

saturday

18 230

Today I feel . . .

sunday

19 231

s	m	t	w	t	f	s
			1	2	3	4
5	6	7	8	9	10	11
12	13	14	15	16	17	18
19	20	21	22	23	24	25
26	27	28	29	30	31	

AUGUST

My mind is a world in itself, which l have peopled with my own creatures.

Lady Caroline Lamb

The New Beacon Book of Quotations by Women, 1996

Untitled, 1973

LAST WEEK . . .
l enjoyed these blessings/triumphs

l faced these challenges/disappointments

THIS WEEK . . .
l will

l will hope for/pray for/meditate on

August

monday

☽ **20** ₂₃₂

Today I feel . . .

tuesday

21 ₂₃₃

Today I feel . . .

wednesday

22 ₂₃₄

Today I feel . . .

thursday

23 ₂₃₅

Today I feel . . .

friday

24 ₂₃₆

Today I feel . . .

saturday

25 ₂₃₇

Today I feel . . .

sunday

26 ₂₃₈

s	m	t	w	t	f	s
			1	2	3	4
5	6	7	8	9	10	11
12	13	14	15	16	17	18
19	20	21	22	23	24	25
26	27	28	29	30	31	

AUGUST

We humans should never forget our capacity to connect with the collective spirit of animals. Their energy is essential to our future growth.

Shirley MacLaine
The New Beacon Book of Quotations by Women, 1996

Untitled, 1979

LAST WEEK . . .
I enjoyed these blessings/triumphs

I faced these challenges/disappointments

THIS WEEK . . .
I will

I will hope for/pray for/meditate on

Aug ✎ Sep

monday

27 239

Today I feel . . .

tuesday

◯ **28** 240

Today I feel . . .

wednesday

29 241

Today I feel . . .

thursday

30 242

Today I feel . . .

friday

31 243

Today I feel . . .

saturday

1 244

Today I feel . . .

sunday

2 245

s	m	t	w	t	f	s
						1
2	3	4	5	6	7	8
9	10	11	12	13	14	15
16	17	18	19	20	21	22
23	24	25	26	27	28	29
30			SEPTEMBER			

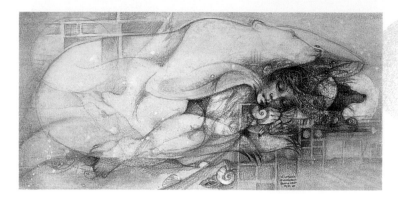

Earth Family, 1990

I f one is lucky a solitary fantasy can totally transform
one million realities.

Maya Angelou
The New Beacon Book of Quotations by Women, 1996

LAST WEEK . . .
I enjoyed these blessings/triumphs

I faced these challenges/disappointments

THIS WEEK . . .
I will

I will hope for/pray for/meditate on

September

LABOR DAY (US, CANADA)

monday

3 246

Today I feel . . .

tuesday

☾ 4 247

Today I feel . . .

wednesday

5 248

Today I feel . . .

thursday

6 249

Today I feel . . .

friday

7 250

Today I feel . . .

saturday

8 251

Today I feel . . .

sunday

9 252

s	m	t	w	t	f	s
						1
2	3	4	5	6	7	8
9	10	11	12	13	14	15
16	17	18	19	20	21	22
23	24	25	26	27	28	29
30			SEPTEMBER			

Untitled, 1976

LAST WEEK . . .

I enjoyed these blessings/triumphs

I faced these challenges/disappointments

THIS WEEK . . .

I will

I will hope for/pray for/meditate on

September

monday

10 253

Today I feel . . .

tuesday

● **11** 254

Today I feel . . .

ROSH HASHANAH (BEGINS AT SUNSET)

wednesday

12 255

Today I feel . . .

thursday

13 256

Today I feel . . .

friday

14 257

Today I feel . . .

saturday

15 258

Today I feel . . .

sunday

16 259

s	m	t	w	t	f	s
						1
2	3	4	5	6	7	8
9	10	11	12	13	14	15
16	17	18	19	20	21	22
23	24	25	26	27	28	29
30						

SEPTEMBER

Illustration from *Buffalo Gals,*
by Ursula LeGuin, 1994

There is no old age. There is, as there always was,
just you.

Carol Matthau
The New Beacon Book of Quotations by Women, 1996

LAST WEEK . . .
I enjoyed these blessings/triumphs

I faced these challenges/disappointments

THIS WEEK . . .
I will

I will hope for/pray for/meditate on

September

monday

17 260

Today I feel . . .

tuesday

18 261

Today I feel . . .

wednesday

☽ **19** 262

Today I feel . . .

thursday

20 263

Today I feel . . .

YOM KIPPUR (BEGINS AT SUNSET)

friday

21 264

Today I feel . . .

saturday

22 265

Today I feel . . .

AUTUMNAL EQUINOX 9:51 AM (GMT)

sunday

23 266

s	m	t	w	t	f	s
						1
2	3	4	5	6	7	8
9	10	11	12	13	14	15
16	17	18	19	20	21	22
23	24	25	26	27	28	29
30						

SEPTEMBER

To dream of the person you would like to be is to waste the person you are.

Anonymous
The Women's Book of Positive Quotations, 2002

Untitled, 1974

LAST WEEK . . .
I enjoyed these blessings/triumphs

I faced these challenges/disappointments

THIS WEEK . . .
I will

I will hope for/pray for/meditate on

September

monday

24 267

Today I feel . . .

tuesday

25 268

Today I feel . . .

wednesday

○ **26** 269

Today I feel . . .

thursday

27 270

Today I feel . . .

friday

28 271

Today I feel . . .

saturday

29 272

Today I feel . . .

sunday

30 273

s	m	t	w	t	f	s
						1
2	3	4	5	6	7	8
9	10	11	12	13	14	15
16	17	18	19	20	21	22
23	24	25	26	27	28	29
30			SEPTEMBER			

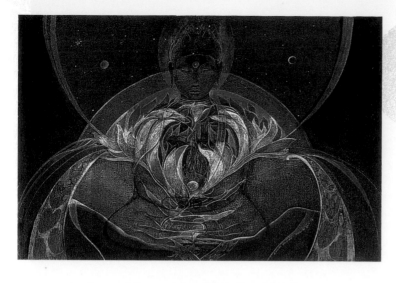

Untitled, 1976

Y̶ou must learn to be still in the midst of
activity, and to be vibrantly alive in repose.

Indira Gandhi
Great Quotes from Great Women, 1997

LAST WEEK . . .
I enjoyed these blessings/triumphs

I faced these challenges/disappointments

THIS WEEK . . .
I will

I will hope for/pray for/meditate on

October

monday

1 274

Today l feel . . .

tuesday

2 275

Today l feel . . .

wednesday

☾ **3** 276

Today l feel . . .

thursday

4 277

Today l feel . . .

friday

5 278

Today l feel . . .

saturday

6 279

Today l feel . . .

sunday

7 280

s	m	t	w	t	f	s
	1	2	3	4	5	6
7	8	9	10	11	12	13
14	15	16	17	18	19	20
21	22	23	24	25	26	27
28	29	30	31			

OCTOBER

It takes a lot of courage to show your dreams to someone else.

Erma Bombeck
The Women's Book of Positive Quotations,
2002

Dragon and Swan, 1975

LAST WEEK . . .
I enjoyed these blessings/triumphs

I faced these challenges/disappointments

THIS WEEK . . .
I will

I will hope for/pray for/meditate on

October

THANKSGIVING DAY (CANADA)

monday

8 281

Today I feel . . .

tuesday

9 282

Today I feel . . .

wednesday

10 283

Today I feel . . .

thursday

● **11** 284

Today I feel . . .

COLUMBUS DAY

friday

12 285

Today I feel . . .

saturday

13 286

Today I feel . . .

sunday

14 287

s	m	t	w	t	f	s
	1	2	3	4	5	6
7	8	9	10	11	12	13
14	15	16	17	18	19	20
21	22	23	24	25	26	27
28	29	30	31			

OCTOBER

Most real relationships are involuntary.

Iris Murdoch

The New Beacon Book of Quotations by Women, 1996

Untitled, 1978

LAST WEEK . . .

I enjoyed these blessings/triumphs

I faced these challenges/disappointments

THIS WEEK . . .

I will

I will hope for/pray for/meditate on

monday

15 ₂₈₈

Today I feel . . .

tuesday

16 ₂₈₉

Today I feel . . .

wednesday

17 ₂₉₀

Today I feel . . .

thursday

18 ₂₉₁

Today I feel . . .

friday

☽ **19** ₂₉₂

Today I feel . . .

saturday

20 ₂₉₃

Today I feel . . .

sunday

21 ₂₉₄

s	m	t	w	t	f	s
	1	2	3	4	5	6
7	8	9	10	11	12	13
14	15	16	17	18	19	20
21	22	23	24	25	26	27
28	29	30	31			

OCTOBER

convivial

Untitled, 1974

LAST WEEK . . .
I enjoyed these blessings/triumphs

I faced these challenges/disappointments

THIS WEEK . . .
I will

I will hope for/pray for/meditate on

October

monday

22 295

Today I feel . . .

tuesday

23 296

Today I feel . . .

UNITED NATIONS DAY

wednesday

24 297

Today I feel . . .

thursday

25 298

Today I feel . . .

friday

○ ## 26 299

Today I feel . . .

saturday

27 300

s	m	t	w	t	f	s
	1	2	3	4	5	6
7	8	9	10	11	12	13
14	15	16	17	18	19	20
21	22	23	24	25	26	27
28	29	30	31			

OCTOBER

Today I feel . . .

SUMMER TIME ENDS (UK)

sunday

28 301

In my end is my beginning.

Mary Stuart
*The Women's Book of Positive
Quotations*, 2002

Untitled, 1977

LAST WEEK . . .
I enjoyed these blessings/triumphs

I faced these challenges/disappointments

THIS WEEK . . .
I will

I will hope for/pray for/meditate on

Oct ❦ Nov

monday

29 302

Today I feel . . .

tuesday

30 303

Today I feel . . .

HALLOWEEN

wednesday

31 304

Today I feel . . .

thursday

☾ 1 305

Today I feel . . .

friday

2 306

Today I feel . . .

saturday

3 307

Today I feel . . .

DAYLIGHT SAVING TIME ENDS

sunday

4 308

s	m	t	w	t	f	s
				1	2	3
4	5	6	7	8	9	10
11	12	13	14	15	16	17
18	19	20	21	22	23	24
25	26	27	28	29	30	

NOVEMBER

Never bend your head. Hold it high. Look the world straight in the eye.

Helen Keller
The Women's Book of Positive Quotations,
2002

Eve, n.d.

LAST WEEK . . .
I enjoyed these blessings/triumphs

I faced these challenges/disappointments

THIS WEEK . . .
I will

I will hope for/pray for/meditate on

November

monday

5 309

Today I feel . . .

tuesday

6 310

Today I feel . . .

wednesday

7 311

Today I feel . . .

thursday

8 312

Today I feel . . .

friday

● **9** 313

Today I feel . . .

saturday

10 314

Today I feel . . .

VETERANS DAY

REMEMBRANCE DAY (CANADA)

sunday

11 315

s	m	t	w	t	f	s
				1	2	3
4	5	6	7	8	9	10
11	12	13	14	15	16	17
18	19	20	21	22	23	24
25	26	27	28	29	30	

NOVEMBER

A nimals were once, for all of us, teachers. They instructed us in ways of being and perceiving that extended our imaginations, that were models for additional possibilities.

Joan McIntyre
The New Beacon Book of Quotations by Women, 1996

Untitled, 1980

LAST WEEK . . .
I enjoyed these blessings/triumphs

I faced these challenges/disappointments

THIS WEEK . . .
I will

I will hope for/pray for/meditate on

November

VETERANS DAY OBSERVED

monday

12 316

Today I feel . . .

tuesday

13 317

Today I feel . . .

wednesday

14 318

Today I feel . . .

thursday

15 319

Today I feel . . .

friday

16 320

Today I feel . . .

saturday

☽ **17** 321

Today I feel . . .

sunday

18 322

s	m	t	w	t	f	s
				1	2	3
4	5	6	7	8	9	10
11	12	13	14	15	16	17
18	19	20	21	22	23	24
25	26	27	28	29	30	

NOVEMBER

Lotus, 1974

LAST WEEK . . .

I enjoyed these blessings/triumphs

I faced these challenges/disappointments

THIS WEEK . . .

I will

I will hope for/pray for/meditate on

November

monday

19 ₃₂₃

Today I feel . . .

tuesday

20 ₃₂₄

Today I feel . . .

wednesday

21 ₃₂₅

Today I feel . . .

THANKSGIVING DAY

thursday

22 ₃₂₆

Today I feel . . .

friday

23 ₃₂₇

Today I feel . . .

saturday

○ **24** ₃₂₈

Today I feel . . .

sunday

25 ₃₂₉

s	m	t	w	t	f	s
				1	2	3
4	5	6	7	8	9	10
11	12	13	14	15	16	17
18	19	20	21	22	23	24
25	26	27	28	29	30	

NOVEMBER

Creative minds have always been known to survive any kind of bad training.

Anna Freud
The Women's Book of Positive Quotations,
2002

Untitled, 1975

LAST WEEK . . .
I enjoyed these blessings/triumphs

I faced these challenges/disappointments

THIS WEEK . . .
I will

I will hope for/pray for/meditate on

Nov ✦ Dec

monday
26 330

Today I feel . . .

tuesday
27 331

Today I feel . . .

wednesday
28 332

Today I feel . . .

thursday
29 333

Today I feel . . .

friday
30 334

Today I feel . . .

saturday
☾ 1 335

Today I feel . . .

sunday
2 336

s	m	t	w	t	f	s
						1
2	3	4	5	6	7	8
9	10	11	12	13	14	15
16	17	18	19	20	21	22
23	24	25	26	27	28	29
30	31					

DECEMBER

T alent is helpful in writing,
but guts are absolutely
necessary.

Jessamyn West
*The New Beacon Book of Quotations
by Women*, 1996

Leopard Shadow, 1987

LAST WEEK . . .
I enjoyed these blessings/triumphs

I faced these challenges/disappointments

THIS WEEK . . .
I will

I will hope for/pray for/meditate on

December

Today I feel . . .

HANUKKAH (BEGINS AT SUNSET)

Today I feel . . .

Today I feel . . .

Today I feel . . .

Today I feel . . .

Today I feel . . .

s	m	t	w	t	f	s
						1
2	3	4	5	6	7	8
9	10	11	12	13	14	15
16	17	18	19	20	21	22
23	24	25	26	27	28	29
30	31			DECEMBER		

All is waiting and all is work; all is change and all is permanence. All is grace.

Barbara Grizzuti Harrison
The New Beacon Book of Quotations by Women, 1996

Untitled, 1976

LAST WEEK . . .
I enjoyed these blessings/triumphs

I faced these challenges/disappointments

THIS WEEK . . .
I will

I will hope for/pray for/meditate on

December

Today I feel . . .

tuesday

11 345

Today I feel . . .

wednesday

12 346

Today I feel . . .

thursday

13 347

Today I feel . . .

friday

14 348

Today I feel . . .

saturday

15 349

Today I feel . . .

sunday

16 350

s	m	t	w	t	f	s
						1
2	3	4	5	6	7	8
9	10	11	12	13	14	15
16	17	18	19	20	21	22
23	24	25	26	27	28	29
30	31				**DECEMBER**	

A woman has got to love a bad man once or twice in her life to be thankful for a good one.

Marjorie Kinnan Rawlings
The Women's Book of Positive Quotations, 2002

Untitled, 1976

LAST WEEK . . .
I enjoyed these blessings/triumphs

I faced these challenges/disappointments

THIS WEEK . . .
I will

I will hope for/pray for/meditate on

December

Today I feel . . .

tuesday

18 352

Today I feel . . .

wednesday

19 353

Today I feel . . .

thursday

20 354

Today I feel . . .

friday

21 355

Today I feel . . .

WINTER SOLSTICE 6:08 AM (GMT)

saturday

22 356

Today I feel . . .

sunday

23 357

s	m	t	w	t	f	s
						1
2	3	4	5	6	7	8
9	10	11	12	13	14	15
16	17	18	19	20	21	22
23	24	25	26	27	28	29
30	31				DECEMBER	

One cannot make oneself, but one can sometimes help a little in the making of somebody else.

Dinah Maria Mulock Craik
The Women's Book of Positive Quotations,
2002

Untitled, 1973

LAST WEEK . . .

I enjoyed these blessings/triumphs

I faced these challenges/disappointments

THIS WEEK . . .

I will

I will hope for/pray for/meditate on

December

monday

◯ **24** 358

Today I feel . . .

CHRISTMAS DAY

tuesday

25 359

Today I feel . . .

BOXING DAY (CANADA, UK)

KWANZAA BEGINS

wednesday

26 360

Today I feel . . .

thursday

27 361

Today I feel . . .

friday

28 362

Today I feel . . .

saturday

29 363

Today I feel . . .

sunday

30 364

s	m	t	w	t	f	s
						1
2	3	4	5	6	7	8
9	10	11	12	13	14	15
16	17	18	19	20	21	22
23	24	25	26	27	28	29
30	31			DECEMBER		

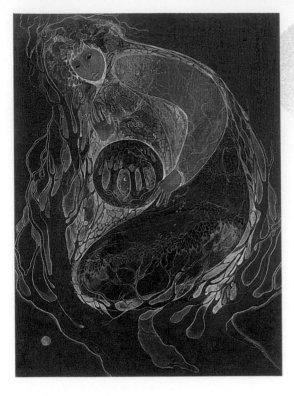

We must not, in trying to think about how we can make a big difference, ignore the small daily differences we can make which, over time, add up to big differences that we often cannot foresee.

Marian Wright Edelman
The Women's Book of Positive Quotations,
2002

Untitled, 1972

LAST WEEK . . .
I enjoyed these blessings/triumphs

I faced these challenges/disappointments

THIS WEEK . . .
I will

I will hope for/pray for/meditate on

monday

☽ **31** ₃₆₅

Today I feel . . .

NEW YEAR'S DAY

tuesday

1 ₁

Today I feel . . .

BANK HOLIDAY (SCOTLAND)

wednesday

2 ₂

Today I feel . . .

thursday

3 ₃

Today I feel . . .

friday

4 ₄

Today I feel . . .

saturday

5 ₅

Today I feel . . .

sunday

6 ₆

s	m	t	w	t	f	s
		1	2	3	4	5
6	7	8	9	10	11	12
13	14	15	16	17	18	19
20	21	22	23	24	25	26
27	28	29	30	31		

JANUARY

2007 International Holidays

Following are the observed dates of major (bank-closing) holidays for selected countries in 2007. Islamic observances are subject to adjustment. Holidays for the US, UK, and Canada and major Jewish holidays appear on this calendar's grid pages. Pomegranate is not responsible for errors or omissions in this list. Users of this information should confirm dates with local sources before making international travel or business plans.

ARGENTINA

1 Jan	New Year's Day
2 Apr	Malvinas Islands Memorial
5 Apr	Holy Thursday
6 Apr	Good Friday
8 Apr	Easter
1 May	Labor Day
25 May	Revolution Day
18 Jun	Flag Day
9 Jul	Independence Day
20 Aug	General San Martín Anniversary
15 Oct	Día de la Raza
8 Dec	Immaculate Conception
25 Dec	Christmas

AUSTRALIA

1 Jan	New Year's Day
26 Jan	Australia Day
5 Mar	Labor Day (WA)
12 Mar	Labor Day (Vic)
	Eight Hours Day (Tas)
19 Mar	Canberra Day (ACT)
6 Apr	Good Friday
7–9 Apr	Easter Holiday
25 Apr	Anzac Day
7 May	Labor Day (Qld)
	May Day (NT)
4 Jun	Foundation Day (WA)
11 Jun	Queen's Birthday
6 Aug	Bank Holiday (NSW, NT)
1 Oct	Labor Day (NSW, ACT, SA)
25 Dec	Christmas
26 Dec	Boxing Day

BRAZIL

1 Jan	New Year's Day
20 Jan	São Sebastião Day (Rio de Janeiro)
25 Jan	São Paulo Anniversary (São Paulo)
19–20 Feb	Carnival
6 Apr	Good Friday
8 Apr	Easter
21 Apr	Tiradentes Day
1 May	Labor Day
7 Jun	Corpus Christi
9 Jul	State Holiday (São Paulo)
7 Sep	Independence Day
12 Oct	Our Lady of Aparecida
2 Nov	All Souls' Day
15 Nov	Proclamation of the Republic
20 Nov	Zumbi dos Palmares Day (Rio de Janeiro)
25 Dec	Christmas

CHINA (SEE ALSO HONG KONG)

1 Jan	New Year's Day
18–20 Feb	Lunar New Year
8 Mar	Women's Day
1–3 May	Labor Day Holiday
4 May	Youth Day
1 June	Children's Day
1 Aug	Army Day
1–3 Oct	National Holiday

FRANCE

1 Jan	New Year's Day
8–9 Apr	Easter Holiday
1 May	Labor Day
8 May	Armistice Day (WWII)
17 May	Ascension Day
27–28 May	Pentecost/Whitmonday
14 Jul	Bastille Day
15 Aug	Assumption Day
1 Nov	All Saints' Day
11 Nov	Armistice Day (WWI)
25 Dec	Christmas

GERMANY

1 Jan	New Year's Day
6 Jan	Epiphany*
6 Apr	Good Friday
8–9 Apr	Easter Holiday
1 May	Labor Day
17 May	Ascension Day
27–28 May	Pentecost/Whitmonday
7 Jun	Corpus Christi*
15 Aug	Assumption Day*
3 Oct	Unity Day
31 Oct	Reformation Day*
1 Nov	All Saints' Day*
21 Nov	Penance Day*
24–26 Dec	Christmas Holiday
31 Dec	New Year's Eve

*Observed only in some states

HONG KONG

1 Jan	New Year's Day
17–20 Feb	Lunar New Year
5 Apr	Ching Ming Festival
6–9 Apr	Easter Holiday
1 May	Labor Day
24 May	Buddha's Birthday
19 Jun	Tuen Ng Day
2 Jul	SAR Establishment Day
26 Sep	Mid-Autumn Festival
1 Oct	Chinese National Holiday
19 Oct	Chung Yeung Festival
25–26 Dec	Christmas Holiday

INDIA

20 Jan	Muharram (Islamic New Year)
26 Jan	Republic Day
31 Mar	Prophet Muhammad's Birthday
	Mahavir Jayanthi
6 Apr	Good Friday
2 May	Buddha Purnima
15 Aug	Independence Day
2 Oct	Mahatma Gandhi's Birthday
13 Oct	Ramzan Id (Eid-al-Fitr)
21 Oct	Dussehra
9 Nov	Diwali (Deepavali)
24 Nov	Guru Nanak's Birthday
20 Dec	Bakr-Id (Eid-al-Adha)
25 Dec	Christmas

Additional holidays to be declared

IRELAND

1 Jan	New Year's Day
17 Mar	St. Patrick's Day
8–9 Apr	Easter Holiday
7 May	May Holiday
4 Jun	June Holiday
6 Aug	August Holiday
29 Oct	October Holiday
25 Dec	Christmas
26 Dec	St. Stephen's Day

ISRAEL

4 Mar	Purim
3 Apr	First day of Pesach
9 Apr	Last day of Pesach
22 Apr	Memorial Day
23 Apr	Independence Day
23 May	Shavuot
24 Jul	Fast of Av
13–14 Sep	Rosh Hashanah
21–22 Sep	Yom Kippur
27 Sep	First day of Sukkot
4–5 Oct	Shemini Atzeret/Simhat Torah

ITALY

1 Jan	New Year's Day
6 Jan	Epiphany
8–9 Apr	Easter Holiday
25 Apr	Liberation Day
1 May	Labor Day
2 Jun	Republic Day
29 Jun	Sts. Peter and Paul (Rome)
15 Aug	Assumption Day
1 Nov	All Saints' Day
8 Dec	Immaculate Conception
25 Dec	Christmas
26 Dec	St. Stephen's Day

2007 International Holidays

JAPAN
1 Jan — New Year's Day
8 Jan — Coming of Age Day
12 Feb — National Foundation Day
21 Mar — Vernal Equinox Holiday
30 Apr — Greenery Day
3 May — Constitution Day
4 May — National Holiday
5 May — Children's Day
16 Jul — Marine Day
17 Sep — Respect for the Aged Day
24 Sep — Autumnal Equinox Holiday
8 Oct — Health and Sports Day
3 Nov — Culture Day
23 Nov — Labor Thanksgiving Day
24 Dec — Emperor's Birthday

KENYA
1 Jan — New Year's Day
6 Apr — Good Friday
8–9 Apr — Easter Holiday
1 May — Labor Day
1 Jun — Madaraka Day
10 Oct — Moi Day
13 Oct — Eid-al-Fitr
20 Oct — Kenyatta Day
12 Dec — Jamhuri Day
25 Dec — Christmas
26 Dec — Boxing Day

MEXICO
1 Jan — New Year's Day
5 Feb — Constitution Day
21 Mar — Benito Juárez's Birthday
5 Apr — Holy Thursday
6 Apr — Good Friday
8 Apr — Easter
1 May — Labor Day
5 May — Battle of Puebla
16 Sep — Independence Day
1 Nov — All Saints' Day
2 Nov — Day of the Dead
20 Nov — Revolution Day
12 Dec — Our Lady of Guadalupe
25 Dec — Christmas

NETHERLANDS
1 Jan — New Year's Day
6 Apr — Good Friday
8–9 Apr — Easter Holiday
30 Apr — Queen's Birthday
4 May — Remembrance Day
5 May — Liberation Day
17 May — Ascension Day
27–28 May — Pentecost/Whitmonday
25–26 Dec — Christmas Holiday

NEW ZEALAND
1–2 Jan — New Year's Holiday
22 Jan — Provincial Anniversary (Wellington)
29 Jan — Provincial Anniversary (Auckland)
6 Feb — Waitangi Day
6 Apr — Good Friday
8–9 Apr — Easter Holiday
25 Apr — Anzac Day
4 Jun — Queen's Birthday
22 Oct — Labor Day
16 Nov — Provincial Anniversary (Canterbury)
25 Dec — Christmas
26 Dec — Boxing Day

NORWAY
1 Jan — New Year's Day
1 Apr — Palm Sunday
5 Apr — Holy Thursday
6 Apr — Good Friday
8–9 Apr — Easter Holiday
1 May — Labor Day
17 May — Ascension Day
         Constitution Day
27–28 May — Pentecost/Whitmonday
25–26 Dec — Christmas Holiday

PUERTO RICO
1 Jan — New Year's Day
6 Jan — Three Kings Day (Epiphany)
8 Jan — Eugenio María de Hostos' Birthday
22 Mar — Emancipation Day
6 Apr — Good Friday
8 Apr — Easter
16 Apr — José de Diego's Birthday
16 Jul — Luís Muñoz Rivera's Birthday
25 Jul — Constitution Day
27 Jul — José Celso Barbosa's Birthday
8 Oct — Día de la Raza
19 Nov — Discovery of Puerto Rico
25 Dec — Christmas
All US federal holidays also observed.

RUSSIA
1–2 Jan — New Year's Holiday
7 Jan — Orthodox Christmas
23 Feb — Soldiers Day
8 Mar — International Women's Day
8 Apr — Orthodox Easter
1–2 May — Spring and Labor Day
9 May — Victory Day
12 Jun — Independence Day
7 Nov — Reconciliation Day
12 Dec — Constitution Day

SINGAPORE
1 Jan — New Year's Day
2 Jan — Hari Raya Haji (Eid-al-Adha)
18–20 Feb — Lunar New Year
6 Apr — Good Friday
8 Apr — Easter
1 May — Labor Day
31 May — Vesak Day (Buddha's Birthday)
9 Aug — National Day
13 Oct — Hari Raya Puasa (Eid-al-Fitr)
9 Nov — Deepavali
20 Dec — Hari Raya Haji (Eid-al-Adha)
25 Dec — Christmas

SOUTH AFRICA
1 Jan — New Year's Day
21 Mar — Human Rights Day
6 Apr — Good Friday
8 Apr — Easter
9 Apr — Family Day
27 Apr — Freedom Day
1 May — Labor Day
16 Jun — Youth Day
9 Aug — National Women's Day
24 Sep — Heritage Day
17 Dec — Day of Reconciliation
25 Dec — Christmas
26 Dec — Day of Goodwill

SPAIN
1 Jan — New Year's Day
6 Jan — Epiphany
19 Mar — St. Joseph's Day
5 Apr — Holy Thursday
6 Apr — Good Friday
8 Apr — Easter
1 May — Labor Day
25 Jul — St. James the Apostle Day
15 Aug — Assumption Day
12 Oct — National Holiday
1 Nov — All Saints' Day
6 Dec — Constitution Day
8 Dec — Immaculate Conception
25 Dec — Christmas

SWITZERLAND
1 Jan — New Year's Day
2 Jan — Berchtold's Day
6 Apr — Good Friday
8–9 Apr — Easter Holiday
17 May — Ascension Day
27–28 May — Pentecost/Whitmonday
1 Aug — National Day
25 Dec — Christmas
26 Dec — St. Stephen's Day

THAILAND
1 Jan — New Year's Day
2 Mar — Makha Bucha Day
6 Apr — Chakri Day
13–15 Apr — Songkran Festival
1 May — Labor Day
         Visakha Bucha Day (Buddha's Birthday)
7 May — Coronation Day
31 Jul — Buddhist Lent Day
13 Aug — Queen's Birthday
23 Oct — Chulalongkorn Day
5 Dec — King's Birthday
10 Dec — Constitution Day
31 Dec — New Year's Eve

2007

JANUARY

s	m	t	w	t	f	s
	1	2	3	4	5	6
7	8	9	10	11	12	13
14	15	16	17	18	19	20
21	22	23	24	25	26	27
28	29	30	31			

MAY

s	m	t	w	t	f	s
		1	2	3	4	5
6	7	8	9	10	11	12
13	14	15	16	17	18	19
20	21	22	23	24	25	26
27	28	29	30	31		

SEPTEMBER

s	m	t	w	t	f	s
						1
2	3	4	5	6	7	8
9	10	11	12	13	14	15
16	17	18	19	20	21	22
23	24	25	26	27	28	29
30						

FEBRUARY

s	m	t	w	t	f	s
				1	2	3
4	5	6	7	8	9	10
11	12	13	14	15	16	17
18	19	20	21	22	23	24
25	26	27	28			

JUNE

s	m	t	w	t	f	s
					1	2
3	4	5	6	7	8	9
10	11	12	13	14	15	16
17	18	19	20	21	22	23
24	25	26	27	28	29	30

OCTOBER

s	m	t	w	t	f	s
	1	2	3	4	5	6
7	8	9	10	11	12	13
14	15	16	17	18	19	20
21	22	23	24	25	26	27
28	29	30	31			

MARCH

s	m	t	w	t	f	s
				1	2	3
4	5	6	7	8	9	10
11	12	13	14	15	16	17
18	19	20	21	22	23	24
25	26	27	28	29	30	31

JULY

s	m	t	w	t	f	s
1	2	3	4	5	6	7
8	9	10	11	12	13	14
15	16	17	18	19	20	21
22	23	24	25	26	27	28
29	30	31				

NOVEMBER

s	m	t	w	t	f	s
				1	2	3
4	5	6	7	8	9	10
11	12	13	14	15	16	17
18	19	20	21	22	23	24
25	26	27	28	29	30	

APRIL

s	m	t	w	t	f	s
1	2	3	4	5	6	7
8	9	10	11	12	13	14
15	16	17	18	19	20	21
22	23	24	25	26	27	28
29	30					

AUGUST

s	m	t	w	t	f	s
			1	2	3	4
5	6	7	8	9	10	11
12	13	14	15	16	17	18
19	20	21	22	23	24	25
26	27	28	29	30	31	

DECEMBER

s	m	t	w	t	f	s
						1
2	3	4	5	6	7	8
9	10	11	12	13	14	15
16	17	18	19	20	21	22
23	24	25	26	27	28	29
30	31					

2008

JANUARY

s	m	t	w	t	f	s
		1	2	3	4	5
6	7	8	9	10	11	12
13	14	15	16	17	18	19
20	21	22	23	24	25	26
27	28	29	30	31		

FEBRUARY

s	m	t	w	t	f	s
					1	2
3	4	5	6	7	8	9
10	11	12	13	14	15	16
17	18	19	20	21	22	23
24	25	26	27	28	29	

MARCH

s	m	t	w	t	f	s
						1
2	3	4	5	6	7	8
9	10	11	12	13	14	15
16	17	18	19	20	21	22
23	24	25	26	27	28	29
30	31					

APRIL

s	m	t	w	t	f	s
		1	2	3	4	5
6	7	8	9	10	11	12
13	14	15	16	17	18	19
20	21	22	23	24	25	26
27	28	29	30			

MAY

s	m	t	w	t	f	s
				1	2	3
4	5	6	7	8	9	10
11	12	13	14	15	16	17
18	19	20	21	22	23	24
25	26	27	28	29	30	31

JUNE

s	m	t	w	t	f	s
1	2	3	4	5	6	7
8	9	10	11	12	13	14
15	16	17	18	19	20	21
22	23	24	25	26	27	28
29	30					

JULY

s	m	t	w	t	f	s
		1	2	3	4	5
6	7	8	9	10	11	12
13	14	15	16	17	18	19
20	21	22	23	24	25	26
27	28	29	30	31		

AUGUST

s	m	t	w	t	f	s
					1	2
3	4	5	6	7	8	9
10	11	12	13	14	15	16
17	18	19	20	21	22	23
24	25	26	27	28	29	30
31						

SEPTEMBER

s	m	t	w	t	f	s
	1	2	3	4	5	6
7	8	9	10	11	12	13
14	15	16	17	18	19	20
21	22	23	24	25	26	27
28	29	30				

OCTOBER

s	m	t	w	t	f	s
			1	2	3	4
5	6	7	8	9	10	11
12	13	14	15	16	17	18
19	20	21	22	23	24	25
26	27	28	29	30	31	

NOVEMBER

s	m	t	w	t	f	s
						1
2	3	4	5	6	7	8
9	10	11	12	13	14	15
16	17	18	19	20	21	22
23	24	25	26	27	28	29
30						

DECEMBER

s	m	t	w	t	f	s
	1	2	3	4	5	6
7	8	9	10	11	12	13
14	15	16	17	18	19	20
21	22	23	24	25	26	27
28	29	30	31			

Notes